To Emily:
I know yo'
appreciate

HILO
LEGENDS

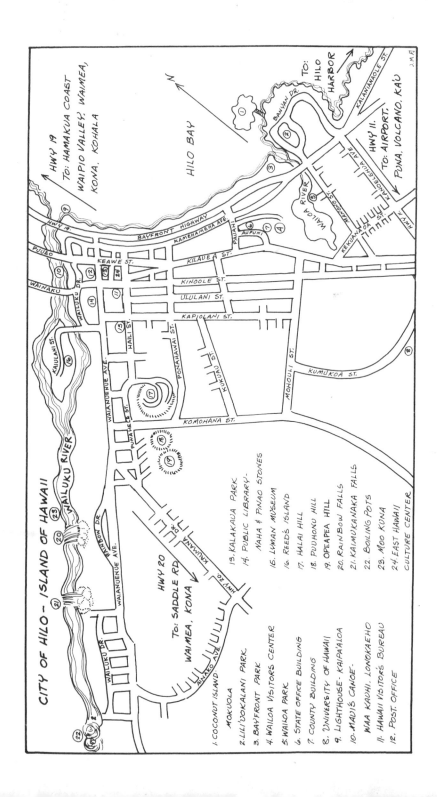

CITY OF HILO - ISLAND OF HAWAII

HILO BAY

HWY 19
TO: HAMAKUA COAST
WAIPIO VALLEY, WAIMEA,
KONA, KOHALA

TO:
HILO
HARBOR

BANYAN DR.

HWY 11
TO: AIRPORT.
PUNA, VOLCANO, KAU

BAYFRONT HIGHWAY
KAMEHAMEHA AVE.
KEAWE ST.
KILAUEA ST.
KINOOLE ST.
ULULANI ST.
KAPIOLANI ST.
KUMUKOA ST.
KOMOHANA ST.

PUEO
WAINAKU
WAILUKU DR.
KAUILANI ST.
WAIANUENUE AVE.
HAILI ST.
PUNAHOA ST.
PONAHAWAI ST.
KUKUAU ST.
MOHOULI ST.

PAUAHI
AUPUNI

MAMO
KEKUANAOA ST.
KAPIOLANI ST.
KANOELEHUA AVE.
KALANIANAOLE ST.
KUMUKOA ST.

WAILUKU RIVER

HWY 20
TO: SADDLE RD.
WAIMEA, KONA

RAINBOW DR.
WAIANUENUE AVE.
WAILUKU DR.
KAUMANA
HWY 20
KANUAHA
APAPANE AVE.

1. COCONUT ISLAND -
   MOKUOLA
2. LILI'UOKALANI PARK
3. BAYFRONT PARK
4. WAILOA VISITOR'S CENTER
5. WAILOA PARK
6. STATE OFFICE BUILDING
7. COUNTY BUILDING
8. UNIVERSITY OF HAWAII
9. LIGHTHOUSE - KAIPALAOA
10. MAUIS CANOE -
    WAA KAUHI, LONOKAEHO
11. HAWAII VISITOR'S BUREAU
12. POST OFFICE
13. KALAKAUA PARK
14. PUBLIC LIBRARY -
    NAHA & PINAO STONES
15. LYMAN MUSEUM
16. REED'S ISLAND
17. HALAI HILL
18. PUUHONO HILL
19. OPEAPEA HILL
20. RAINBOW FALLS
21. KAIMUKANAKA FALLS
22. BOILING POTS
23. MOO KUNA
24. EAST HAWAII
    CULTURE CENTER

N

WAILOA RIVER

HILO LEGENDS

Retold by
FRANCES REED

Illustrated by
JAN MOON

Published by
PETROGLYPH PRESS, LTD.

ISBN 912180-45-5

Published by
THE PETROGLYPH PRESS, LTD.
201 Kinoole Street
Hilo, Hawaii 96720
reedbook@interpac.net

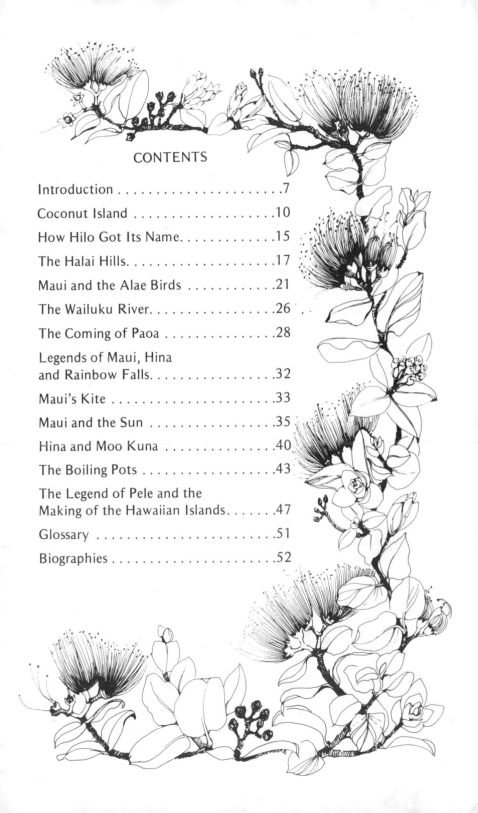

CONTENTS

HILO LEGENDS
by
Frances K. Reed

On the eastern side of the Island of Hawaii there is a crescent-shaped bay along the shore of which the old town of Hilo nestles snugly against the sloping hills. Once there was a beautiful black sand beach following the curvature of the bay, and the Polynesian people, migrating from their homeland far to the south, lived and worked and played here for perhaps a thousand years before the islands were discovered by the English explorer, Captain James Cook, in 1778 and forever changed.

Now the black sand beach is nearly gone, replaced first by railroad tracks and now by a modern highway which goes entirely around the Big Island, as the Island of Hawaii is best known.

The Pacific Ocean, usually lapping gently against the rocky shore, has not always been kind to Hilo. Tsunamis, or tidal waves, generated by earthquakes thousands of miles away, have often sent huge walls of water crashing against the town. In 1946 and again in 1960 large parts of Hilo were destroyed, only to be rebuilt. In earlier times there was no warning, as there is today, that these waves were on the way, so the people living close to the ocean were always aware that at any moment it could send its destructive power to destroy their homes and their lives.

But it was perhaps not the ocean but the volcanos that inspired the most awe. Towering over their village were the two mountains, Mauna Loa and Mauna Kea. The latter, the white mountain, so named because it was often capped with snow, caused them little concern, as it showed no sign of volcanic activity. However, Mauna Loa, the long mountain, sometimes sent rivers of fiery lava toward Hilo. As late as 1881 one such flow had entered the edge of the town, destroying the homes and gardens in its path.

And so the native Hawaiians, their lives closely controlled by the mysterious forces of nature, turned to interpreting the unexplainable by creating myths and legends that were passed down through the generations. Many of these stories, told for hundreds of years, center on physical landmarks that can still be found in the Hilo area. These are the legends that you will find retold once again in this book.

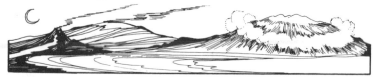

Looking down on Old Hilo Town are three hills, tiny in comparison to the giant mountains at their backs, bearing the names Halai, Opeapea and Puu Honu, but usually called the Halai Hills. They are extinct volcanic craters, created in prehistoric times during eruptions of Mauna Loa. Nearby is the Wailuku River and beautiful Rainbow Falls, the home, it was believed, of the goddess Hina and her demigod son, Maui.

Many of the tales of Hilo are of Hina and Maui and his brothers and sisters. And on rain-shrouded days, when the hills and mountains are buried in mist and the Wailuku River roars to the sea, one senses that the ghosts of these ancient gods still watch over Old Hilo Town. Knowing the stories that were told so long ago will give new interest and meaning as one walks along the river, watches the Boiling Pots, gazes at Rainbow Falls, or explores Coconut Island.

These legends have been told with many variations, as legends always are. This retelling is a composite of the versions that I have read. My three chief sources, all long out of print, were:

Legends of the Wailuku, by Charlotte Hapai,
    1920 (reprinted as Hilo Legends in 1966)
Ghosts of the Hilo Hills, by W. D. Westervelt
    (reprinted in 1968)
Legends and Stories of Hawaii, by Lorna J.
    Desha and others, no date   ●

COCONUT ISLAND

Long ago a flow of lava from the volcano Mauna Loa reached the ocean and as it hardened formed a reef or ledge in Hilo Bay. The higher parts of the reef became little rock islands. The largest of these, now known as Coconut Island, was originally called Mokuola by the early Hawaiians. There they built a place of refuge, and persons who fled to the island were safe from the dangers of enemies and punishment. On the shore of Hilo Bay near Mokuola stood a heiau or temple, and the whole area was considered by the people as sacred to their gods.

Later on, when belief in the ancient religion had been put aside, the Island of Mokuola became a favorite gathering place for play and swimming. Today it is called Coconut Island and is a county park, across from Liliuokalani Park and reached only by a foot bridge near the Hilo Hawaiian Hotel. Older Hawaiians may remember that the name Mokuola means "island which makes one get well" and look for that certain rock in one of the inlets which, if one swam around it, would cure illnesses.

There is a legend about Coconut Island that has nothing to do with its origin as a part of a lava flow. It was told that Maui, the powerful young demigod who lived with his mother, the goddess Hina, in the great cave below Rainbow Falls, owned not only a magic canoe but also a magic fishhook. With his canoe he could cover the distance between the islands of Hawaii and Maui with only two sweeps of his paddle; with his fishhook he could catch all the fish in the sea and leave none for anyone else.

One day, as he watched another canoe set out on its difficult journey to the island of Maui, he wondered to himself if it might not be better to have all the islands joined together, making it possible for his people to travel to any part of the kingdom with less effort.

Calling a meeting of Hawaii's chiefs and strong men, Maui informed them of a plan to draw all the islands together. He told them that he would need their help in the pulling, but no matter how long it took or how hard it was, they must never look back to see how much was being accomplished until the islands were firmly joined.

The men promised to obey and at once proceeded to their new task. The island now known as Maui, the one closest to Hawaii, was chosen for the first attempt. Maui, the demigod, fastened his magic fishhook into that part of the island of Maui nearest the island of Hawaii and at his command the strong men and chiefs paddled with all their might. Slowly the island moved behind them.

No one dared to look back, though all were eager to see the result of their struggles. Long and steadily they paddled until the two islands were only a few feet apart. Then one of the chiefs could no longer restrain his curiosity and turned his head.

In an instant the charm was broken; the island of Maui slid back through the sea to its former position in spite of all that Maui, the chiefs, and the strong men could do to stop it. Only a small piece of it was left, that in which the fishhook was still deeply imbedded.

And that is how, according to legend, Coconut Island, once a part of Maui, happens to be in Hilo Bay.

HOW HILO GOT ITS NAME

King Kamehameha was a great warrior, whose chief ambition, which he lived to realize, was to become the ruler of all the Hawaiian Islands. Naturally, he had numerous enemies, and he never remained long in one place for fear that some of them might learn of his whereabouts and attack him.

One time when he was camped near the mouth of the Wailuku, he planned to visit a special friend who lived a short way up the river on what is now known as Reed's Island. As the man was a powerful chief, Kamehameha felt safe in going to him without his usual bodyguards. Before leaving camp he called to his servants and told them to stand watch over his canoe so that it would not be stolen or carried away by the tide. This they promised to do.

As the hours passed and the king did not return or send word to his men, they grew uneasy about him. Perhaps he had been ambushed or had fallen into one of the caverns formed by ancient lava flows, which are often treacherously concealed by a thin, brittle crust that a man of Kamehameha's size would easily break through. As much as they feared for the king's safety, the servants dared not leave the canoe unattended. They were in a quandary.

"I know what we can do!" cried one of the men. "We will make a rope of ti leaves and tie the canoe so it cannot drift away."

"Make a rope?" queried another. "How can we do that?"

"Simple enough," answered the first speaker; "I'll show you. Take the ti leaves and fasten them together. First you make two chains of leaves, like this, and then twist each one. When you place them together, they will naturally twine about each other and you have a very strong rope. Such twisting is called 'hilo.'"

With these sturdy ropes they tied the canoe to the point of land known to the old Hawaiians as Kaipaʻaloa, near the mouth of the Wailuku River where a lighthouse stands today. Then the men set out to search for the king.

Only a short way up the river they met Kamehameha returning unharmed. Not realizing why they were coming toward him, the king demanded, "Where is my canoe? You promised to guard it. By now it may have drifted out to sea or been stolen!"

"We tied it with ti ropes," answered the servants.

"Ti ropes," roared his majesty. "No one here knows how to make ropes like that. The only place where they do know is at Waipio. How did you learn?"

"I came to you from there," answered the man who had taught the others to make the ropes.

"So that is how you know. Well and good. From now on this place shall be called Hilo."

And so it has been. The town at the mouth of the Wailuku River has since that day been known by the Hawaiian word meaning "to twist."   ●

THE HALAI HILLS

Long ago Mauna Loa volcano created three cinder cones that became known as the Halai Hills. Once they rose above the town of Hilo and were the subject of legends that the Hawaiians love to tell. Now they themselves are covered with houses and the city surrounds them. Haili Street ends at the foot of the largest of these hills, the one called Halai. The others are Opeapea and Puu Honu. A crater inside Halai is called the Imu of Hina. This legend tells us why.

Halai was the home of Hina Ke Ahi, eldest daughter of the goddess Hina, who lived in the cave behind Rainbow Falls. She was also the sister of Maui, the demigod, who appears in most of the ancient stories. Another sister was Hina Kuluua, whose domain was the smaller hill of Puu Honu, and who was very jealous of Hina Ke Ahi.

Hina Ke Ahi ruled over Halai wisely and well. She was kind to her people and in return dearly loved by them. They were industrious and contented, planting their taro, potatoes and bananas, and raising hogs and dogs. The women kept busy making tapa cloth from the bark of trees.

But there came a time when there was no rain for months on end. The crops began to shrivel and die. There was no food for the people, and they were weak with hunger. Hina Ke Ahi knew that unless something was done they would all die.

A plan came to her mind. She told the people to gather all the firewood they could find and then dig a large cooking oven, an imu. The wood went into it and a fire lighted. It burned until the stones on the bottom were red hot.

Then Hina Ke Ahi looked at her anxious people and said, "I am about to make an offering to the gods. No help can come to you unless I give myself to be sacrificed in the imu. When I have stepped inside you must cover me up quickly and do not stop until the last bit of smoke is hidden. In three days a woman will appear at the edge of the imu and tell you what to do."

The people did as they had been commanded
and then anxiously waited beside the imu.

When Hina Ke Ahi disappeared into the imu
she was not harmed by the fire, for she was a
goddess of fire. She traveled about underground
and came up to the surface several times. Halai
Hill trembled, and earthquakes shook the land
round about. Once she caused a great spring of
sweet water to burst forth in the path of the
ocean surf. This was named Hina Auauwai in
her honor.

On the third day after Hina's disappearance,
her people began to look for a strange woman to
come to them. Soon they saw a person resembling
their beloved goddess approaching and heard her
tell them to uncover the imu. When they did, to
their great surprise and joy, they found an abundant supply of food. The imu was left uncovered
to show how help had come to the starving
people, and to this day the crater of Halai is
known as Imu-o-Hina.

When the famine reached Puu Honu, Hina
Kulana wanted to prove that she was as powerful
as her sister, although she was a goddess of rain,
not of fire. In spite of that she commanded that
an imu be dug and disappeared into it exactly as
Hina Ke Ahi had done. The next day a dark cloud
hung over the imu, hiding it from view. On the
third day the cloud was still there, even though
elsewhere it was bright and sunny. The people
waited hopefully, but no one appeared to them.
Night came, then dawn. Finally, the people could

wait no longer. They uncovered the imu and there lay the ashes of their queen. They could not be saved from the famine and so they covered the imu again. That is why Puu Honu has no crater like that of Halai.

Hina Ke Ahi felt very sad for her sister's people, for she knew that if Hina Kulana had used her own power, the rain, she would have provided food for them. But she had tried to rival her sister and had brought death to herself and her people. It was too late for Hina Ke Ahi to help, but she composed a chant in memory of her sister, one that was long sung by Hawaiians. ❁

MAUI AND THE ALAE BIRDS

There was a time, long ago, when the people of Hilo were unable to make fire and everything was eaten raw. Without fire they could not cook their breadfruit, sweet potatoes, fish and even the taro, which stung their mouths.

On the southern side of Halai Hill folks often used to see thin white smoke rising among the ferns. But children and others who ran to find the queer little white cloud in the bushes saw only some frightened alae birds flying away. There was nothing left but ashes and blackened sticks. Sometimes a little boy named Holopaani would find a bit of roasted banana that had been left in the ashes. He would taste it and give some to his

sister, Makahinuhinu, and then he would say, "Oh, if we could only find out how the alae birds do this! If only we knew how they make the fire and cook the banana! My, how good it tastes!"

But try as they might, none could make fire, none but the alae birds, and they were too smart to be caught at it. Even Maui tried for a long time, but he did not succeed. The birds knew that he watched them and they were always on the lookout for him. They called him Maui Mama, which means Maui, the quick one. They would not make a fire until they saw him go off to fish with his brothers in Hilo Bay.

One day Maui said to his brothers, "I have thought of something. You take the long calabash in which we keep our nets and put it between you in the canoe. Then go out to fish and leave me on shore. The alae will think, 'Ah, now we are safe! There are three men out fishing.' But I will go slyly up to their place on Halai to watch for them. I will fool them this time."

So Maui crept up under the tall ama'u ferns and hid before the alae came.

Very soon the alae birds flew swiftly by with their leader, Huapi, the active one. She alone knew the fire secret. "Hurry, Alae Huapi!" cried the others. "Kindle your fire. Let us put the bananas in quickly before Maui Mama can come back from fishing and catch us."

Maui heard every word of this, but he was not quite quick enough to see the fire started, even though he was hiding close by, behind a big rock.

However, he leaped out to catch a burning stick. The watch-bird saw him and screamed, "Put out the fire!" In a moment the fire was out and the alae birds were flying away like the wind. Only brave little Alae Huapi stayed a moment longer to scratch out the very last spark of fire.

Maui grabbed her. "Ah ha, I've caught you now," said he, holding her in his big hand. "Now tell me how you make fire." The alae bird fluttered and struggled and twisted but would not speak. "Tell me, tell me," cried Maui, pinching the poor bird. "Tell me or I will kill you."

Then the alae bird spoke. "Yes, I will tell you. Get a stick and a banana leaf. Rub the leaf with the stick and fire will come. Maui held the little alae safely in one hand and went to work with the other to rub and rub. The alae looked on with a laugh hiding in her eyes.

Did Maui get fire that way? No, he did not. He became angry instead and shook the little bird until she could hardly speak.

"Now then," said he, "look out, if you don't tell me the truth this time!" Alae answered, "Bring some taro stalks and rub them with your stick." Again she looked on with laughing eyes as Maui found that all he could get was water. A long groove was made in the taro stalk. Anyone who looks for this groove can see it even today. Maui was getting properly fooled, so he slapped the alae and shook her even harder, but she kept her secret.

At last Maui turned to her and said, "Now, I will try rubbing your head and see what I shall get." He scraped away until the blood flowed down, and ever since then all alae birds have had a red spot on their heads where once it was white.

Poor, plucky little Alae Huapi. She was sadly bruised and bleeding. This time she said, "Go get a very dry branch of hau and rub it with your stick." Maui rubbed long and well. The branch grew warm, then hot and, at last, in the fine soft dust made by his scratching, a tiny spark glowed. Here, finally, was fire for his mother, Hina, and fire for all the people of the land. ✺

THE WAILUKU RIVER

The Wailuku River is fed from a vast water-shed, the densely wooded lower slopes and often snow-capped peaks of Mauna Loa and Mauna Kea. Flowing through Hilo, the water tumbles down a series of falls, finally joining the ocean near the north end of Hilo Bay, at the edge of "old downtown." As it goes through the city it is spanned by three bridges, one just at its mouth. This is often called "the singing bridge" because of the humming sound that occurs as car tires cross the metal grid of its floor. In Hawaiian Wailuku means "destroying water."

In earlier times, before there were any bridges or other safeguards, the river, during storms, often did great damage to property and sometimes took lives. Legends connected with the Wailuku con-firm the belief that it was indeed named for its frequently violent behaviour.

Long ago, so one legend tells, a fearful dragon named Moo Kuna blocked the gorge below Rain-bow Falls in an attempt to drown the goddess Hina, who lived in the great cave for which the falls form a curtain. How her son, the demigod Maui, came to her rescue and then hunted down Moo Kuna and killed him is told in the legend "The Last of Moo Kuna."

When Paoa, a powerful god from Tahiti, came to visit Hawaii, he built a grass hut and made his home on the long, low rock now known as "Maui's Canoe," in the Wailuku near its mouth.

Local gods thought the selection of the home-site unwise. Paoa was unaware of the sudden and rapid rise of the river when cloudbursts of rain loosed torrents upon the slopes of Mauna Kea. Hina, goddess of the river, warned the visitor of his danger and told him how the angry waters would sweep everything before them. In the legend "The Coming of Paoa" you will find his answer.

In those days there must have been more water in the river than there is today, for some of it is now diverted to turbines that produce electricity. But in spite of the decreased volume, the river is still often violent and treacherous, rolling down huge boulders and tearing out trees along its sides and carrying them to the sea, thus living up to its name "Destroying Water." ●

THE COMING OF PAOA

Many years ago there lived on the Island of Tahiti several brothers, all very gifted and powerful gods of that land. One named Paoa was overcome by grief when his only son was killed and decided to leave Tahiti and seek peace on another island.

In preparation for a long journey by canoe he took only three things with him: two kinds of fish, the aku and the opelu, and some pili grass. Journeying northward he encountered a terrific storm, which grew more violent as the days passed. Sometimes it seemed that the low canoe

could no longer breast the great mountains of angry water that bore down upon it, as though to drive it under and swallow it in the black depths.

Fearing for his safety, Paoa took the two kinds of fish, a few of each, and threw them overboard.

Almost at once the mighty waves were calmed and the canoe went on its way through peaceful water, while the storm raged on all sides, a little distance away.

Even today if you are out on the ocean and see a smooth area of water in the midst of a rough sea, you will know that there is a school of aku or opelu very near the surface.

So Paoa sailed safely through the storm. As soon as it subsided, he called back the fish and placed them in his canoe once more. They had been very helpful and might be of use should the storm arise again.

At last Paoa came to an island which appeared very large and was covered with vegetation. Paddling his canoe into a great crescent-shaped bay, he saw a river emptying into it and turned the nose of his tiny craft that way. Not far up the river he came to a long, low rock now known as Ka Waa o Maui (The Canoe of Maui).

So great was the joy of Paoa upon reaching this beautiful island that he decided to make it his home. To commemorate his safe landing he at once planted on the rock the pili grass that he had brought with him. Also, he freed his aku and opelu fishes in the new waters, where in time they multiplied to countless millions.

Very soon he built for himself a grass hut and was careful to tend the pili grass, which grew rapidly and before long spread to other parts of Paoa's new island home.

Hawaiians soon learned to use the pili grass in

house building, as it made a tighter thatch and lasted longer than the grasses to which they had been accustomed.

Farther up the river, which Paoa learned was named Wailuku, there lived the goddess Hina. Soon after the arrival of this stranger from Tahiti, Hina heard of him and his chosen home. Evidently he had not come to wage war or do harm to the people, for he had already made friends with the fishermen living near him.

So Hina decided to see for herself and went down to his home. She was surprised to find that he really had established himself on the low rock.

"You must not stay on this rock!" she exclaimed. "Can't you see the waters above here are high? When the rains come you will be washed away and drowned. It is not safe."

Paoa stood upon the little plot of pili grass as he answered her. "No, I will not go away, for no matter how high the waters come they shall never cover this spot."

From that day on Paoa's word held true. No matter how high the Wailuku River rises, the legends say, it has never covered the little plot of pili grass which still grows on the long, low rock near the river's mouth. ●

THE LEGENDS OF MAUI, HINA
AND RAINBOW FALLS

Maui, the demigod, was strong and wise. He loved to help his mother, the goddess Hina, who lived in a cave behind Rainbow Falls. With his great power he could change his form and go as far and as fast as he pleased. There are many stories telling about his brave deeds. ●

MAUI'S KITE

There were days when Maui was restless and time hung heavy upon his hands. Adventure seemed to be in hiding and Maui yearned for some excitement in his life.

It was then that Laamaomao, god of the winds, who lived not far above Rainbow Falls in the beautiful gorge of the Wailuku River, suggested that Maui build a kite, a large kite. He, Laamaomao, would see that there would be winds to fly the kite wherever Maui wanted to go.

So Maui started the construction of an enormous kite. Hina made a beautiful and strong kapa (bark cloth) and twisted the fibers of the olona plant into a strong cord. Willing helpers made a frame from the red wood of a koa tree, and in due time the big plaything was ready.

Laamaomao, who had eagerly watched the progress of his idea, was ready, too. He directed a steady, gentle breeze up the gorge. Gracefully and birdlike, the kite rose into the brilliant turquoise sky, and as it soared and dipped and circled, Maui's delight knew no bounds. In the days that followed, Laamaomao occasionally increased the force of his blasts, and the kite floated farther and farther away. Maui gloried in the tussle as the winds tossed his treasure among the clouds.

OLONA

Sometimes Maui would tire of his sport and, drawing its cord through a round hole in a rock which lay in the center of a small lake near the wind caves, would leave his kite to its own devices while he slept.

On one such occasion Laamaomao, having received an order for a great storm, forgot all about Maui's kite and turned loose his most powerful wind. All night long it howled through the creaking trees, driving the rain before it in lashing sheets. Stout as it was, the olona cord with which Maui's kite was moored could not long withstand the strain and finally parted, leaving the kite to the mercy of the winds. Tossed madly about in the storm, it was carried far across the flank of Mauna Loa and dropped into the southern sea off the shore of Ka'u.

Great was Maui's surprise and consternation when he found his kite gone. He set out at once in search of it, and after many days found it where it had been hidden by Puuanuhe, the much-dreaded lizard woman who made her home on the shores of the Ka'u Desert. Then Maui returned home with his precious toy and fastened it more securely than ever. The legend goes on to say that the immense kite eventually turned to stone, but no one today knows where that stone is located. ◉

MAUI AND THE SUN

While Maui was away chasing his kite, his
mother, Hina, and her women were making kapa
from the bark of wauke and mamaki trees. First
they soaked the bark and scraped off the green
outside skin. They pounded the white inside
part with their hard wooden beaters on the kapa
boards. All day long their busy tapping could be
heard. The bark grew thin and spread out to form
a narrow strip of cloth. Then the narrow strips
were joined together to form a wide kapa and
dyes were applied for decoration.

But often the kapa was still damp when the sun was going down in the west. Then it had to be gathered in and often fine pieces were smeared and ruined. "It is always so," the women cried. "The sun goes too quickly. The night comes and brings rain; the kapa never dries."

Just then Maui returned from Ka'u with his kite. When he saw the sad faces of the women, he asked, "What is the matter? What happened while I was away chasing my kite?"

"Oh, nothing new," replied Hina. "It is the stubborn sun, always hurrying on too fast and never waiting for our kapa to dry. Can't you make him go more slowly, Maui?"

"Yes, I'm sure that I can," answered Maui. The demigod knew that to accomplish this he would need to go to the Island of Maui on which is situated Haleakala, today the greatest dormant volcanic crater in the world, and in ancient times known as "The House of the Sun." First, he twisted a long, fine cord of coconut fiber, and everyone thought that he was about to launch his canoe in Hilo Bay and begin his journey.

But Maui had other plans. He said to himself, "The sun must not see me coming toward his house. He might suspect danger. I will take another form." Then he hid for a moment and changed himself into a beautiful white rooster. The rooster rose from the bushes on the beach and flew swiftly over the island of Hawaii and then over the blue channel of Alenuihaha, which lies between Maui and Hawaii. At evening it reached Makena on Maui.

Meanwhile, the hurrying sun spied the rooster but could see no danger in the flying white bird, so he sank quickly to sleep in his mountain house. He did not dream that the rooster had changed back into Maui Mama, the fleet one, who was now ready for his midnight journey through the uplands.

Maui hastened up the grassy slopes of the kula lands of Makawao. He climbed the steep, rocky sides of Haleakala until he reached the top. There in the great crater in the middle of the mountain lay the sun, fast asleep. Light clouds covered him.

Maui looked about and found a cave near the path. Here he hid and watched for the sun to awaken and start on his early morning journey across the sky.

The sun had one leg which was much longer than the others. This was the first ray of the sunrise. Maui watched for this ray.

Soon, up rose King Sun, shining rosy red on the soft, fleecy clouds that rolled away to let him pass. Suddenly, Maui sprang out of his hiding place, swinging his twisted lasso, and in less than a moment caught the sun's long, swift leg.

"Who are you and what do you want?" cried the sun angrily. "What is this mischief you are doing? Let me loose! I have many duties and must hurry on my way!"

But Maui held the cord fast. He would not let

the sun go. "You must first make an agreement
with me," he said. "I will let you loose when

you promise to go more slowly every day so my mother Hina's kapa will dry."

"No, indeed, I will not promise you that," replied the sun, and he kept on struggling to free himself from Maui.

Then Maui became angry and with his strong magic club struck off the sun's long leg, leaving him with only the short ones which could not go so fast.

"Now," said Maui, quickly throwing the lasso again, "you will go slowly to suit Hina. Also, you must not shine too hot in the long, bright days. You must not kill the young potato or the tender taro or the budding banana with your fierce, burning rays."

"Oh, yes, yes indeed, I will promise if only you will let me go," begged the sun.

After much argument they agreed to compromise. The sun promised to go slowly six months of the year and then, for the remaining six, to hurry as fast as before.

Maui was content with this arrangement and, pleased with his success, permitted the sun to proceed on his journey. Then he returned as fast as he could go with the good news for his mother. From then on, at least during half of the year, the lovely soft kapa would dry all in one afternoon and be ready for the dyes with which beautiful designs were painted upon it. That afternoon the grateful women started to work on a piece of soft kapa with which they would make a new cape for Maui. The cloth dried in one afternoon. ●

HINA AND MOO KUNA

Far above Rainbow Falls there lived a powerful dragon named Moo Kuna. He had the slippery body of a lizard and was large and ugly to look at.

Moo Kuna often tormented the goddess Hina in her rocky cave behind Rainbow Falls by sending over great torrents of water or by rolling logs and boulders down the stream. Quite often he would block the river below the falls with sediment sent down by freshets during the rainy season.

But Hina was well protected. Her cave was large, and the misty cloud of spray from the falling waters helped to conceal it. Also, she had a servant cloud, Ao-Opua, that guarded her abode. If Hina was in trouble, this cloud would rise high above the falls, showing an unusual shape. Whenever Maui saw this warning cloud, he would hurry home to his mother.

One night, while Maui was fishing in Hilo Bay, a great storm arose. The angry waters rushed and

roared about the mouth of Hina's cave. Seizing the opportunity, Moo Kuna lifted a huge boulder and hurled it over the cliffs. It fit perfectly where it fell between the walls of the gorge and blocked the rush of the torrent. The cold water rose higher and higher until it reached Hina's sleeping quarters.

The goddess sprang to her feet, calling for help. Her cries of panic grew louder and louder until they were heard by Maui. Through the darkness he could see the warning cloud. With his mother's cries ringing in his ears, he paddled to the shore. He needed only two strokes of his magic paddle to land at the mouth of the Wailuku River.

The long, narrow rock in the river just below the middle bridge is called Ka Waa o Maui, the Canoe of Maui, and is located where Maui is supposed to have run it aground at the foot of the rapids.

Seizing the magic club, with which he had conquered the sun, Maui rushed to the scene of danger to his mother. Seeing the rock blocking the river, he raised his club and struck it a mighty blow. The rock split in two, allowing the strong current to rush unhindered on its way.

Hearing the crash of the club and realizing that his attempt on the life of Hina had failed, Kuna turned and fled up the river.

The remains of the great boulder, now known as Lonokaeho, overgrown with tropical plants and with the river rushing through the rift, lie there to this day as proof of Maui's strength.   ●

THE BOILING POTS

So great was the wrath of Maui at the attempt by Kuna to drown his mother that he vowed to find the monster and kill him on sight.

Kuna had fled to a hiding place far up the river, trembling at the thought of capture by the mighty demigod who, as he approached, shook the earth with his heavy tread. Then Kuna heard the voice of Maui calling, "Come forth at once, Kuna."

Soon Maui stood before the hole in which the monster lay hiding. Catching sight of him, Maui let out a deafening yell, poised his magic spear, and with one sweep of his mighty arm, hurled it into the depths of Kuna's cavern. But the dragon, sly and agile, slipped out in time to save himself.

Wasting no time, Kuna started downstream with Maui in hot pursuit, spearing his quarry from one hole to another. Diving into one of several deep pools in the river, Kuna hoped that at last he was safely hidden. Maui was not to be thus easily fooled. He could see the grotesque bulk of his enemy far below the surface of the gloomy water. Kuna was cornered.

Calling upon Pele, goddess of the volcano, to send him hot stones and molten lava, Maui cast these into Kuna's retreat until the waters boiled furiously, sending a vast column of steam far above the rim of the gorge.

Known today as the Boiling Pots, although time has cooled their waters, these pools still bubble and surge as vigorously as ever, especially when the heavy rains come and remind them of

the time when Kuna the Dragon sought refuge
within their depths.

Tough as the hide of Kuna was, it could not
save him from the terrific heat generated by the
red hot rocks and lava cast into the pool by Maui.
Burned and nearly exhausted, the monster man-
aged to drag himself from the cauldron and
continue his flight downstream. Maui sent torrents of boiling water after him, scalding at last
the life from his ugly body.

Then Maui rolled the huge carcass down the
river to a point below Rainbow Falls, within sight
of his mother's home, where she could view daily
the evidence that no one might threaten her and
live.

And there the ungainly form lies today, a
long, black rock island known as Moo Kuna, between the rapids where every freshet, every heavy

rain, beats upon it as though in everlasting punishment for plotting the death of the beloved
goddess, Hina.

THE LEGEND OF PELE
AND
THE MAKING OF THE HAWAIIAN ISLANDS

Countless centuries ago there lived in Kahiki, in the southern Pacific Ocean, a fire goddess named Pele. She had the power to cause great earthquakes and to send fountains of lava up from the ocean floor, thus creating new lands as she moved about.

Eventually she wearied of her homeland and, yearning for new adventures, set sail to the north, accompanied by her many brothers and sisters. When she reached the part of the Pacific Ocean where the Hawaiian Islands now lie, she decided to make a new home for herself.

First, she created the island of Kauai and lived on a mountain called Waialeale, which means Rippling Water. While there she formed other little islands nearby, one that is now called Niihau.

Next, she moved in a southeasterly direction and built up the island of Oahu. There she lived for a very long time, moving about to various parts of the island, throwing up new mountains as she went.

But Pele was not yet satisfied. Continuing in the same direction, she spent a long time creating the island of Maui. On top of its huge mountain she formed a crater so that the sun could live near her forever. It is called Haleakala, House of the Sun.

For a while Pele was content. For amusement she would throw rocks and lava flows far out into the sea. Molokai, Lanai and Kahoolawe were

formed. But she knew that she had not yet created her masterpiece.

Assembling her brothers and sisters, she laid her plans for a larger island with higher mountains for their final home. Together they left Maui and started to build the Island of Hawaii. First came the Kohala Mountains, then Mauna Kea, the highest island peak in the world, Pele's pride. Later on it was Hualalai and then Mauna Loa and finally Kilauea.

Her favorite flowers are the lehua blossoms of the ohia trees.   These grow best in the rocks around the craters and on the rough lava flows along the slopes of the mountains. Pele treasures these bright red blooms and her akuas guard them zealously. To punish those who pluck the flowers she sends down the rain.

Now, according to the legends, Pele has two favorite homes. One is the summit of Mauna Loa and is called Mokuaweoweo, and the other is the firepit of Kilauea, named Halemaumau.

Pele, the legends continue, sometimes takes the form of an ugly old woman and as such wanders along the seacoast asking for food and shelter. If the inhabitants selfishly deny her these things, she causes lava flows that destroy their homes and gardens, but upon good, kind people she bestows her blessings, giving them abundant food, happiness and long life.

Pele was ever a kindly older sister who loved her brothers and sisters dearly. She did not forget her promise to them to find each a home. Starting from the seacoast of Puna, she built a series of craters, ending near her home, Halemaumau in Kilauea, one for each member of her family. Today these craters are known as The Chain of Craters, and each bears the name of the brother or sister whose home it was.

To many people in Hawaii, Pele lives on, still creating an ever larger island. When a red glow lights up the sky over Puna or Kilauea or the slopes of Mauna Loa and the hot lava pushes up from the center of the earth, flowing into craters or over the palis into the sea, Hiloans will say, "Pele's at it again." But this will be said more in admiration than in fear, for many believe that Pele continues to watch over their city by the crescent-shaped bay and keeps her fiery destruction from reaching it. ⬤

GLOSSARY

aku	skipjack tuna
akua	god or goddess, spirit
alae	mudhen or coot (bird)
ama'u	fern
hau	lowland tree
heiau	temple, place of worship
hilo	to twist, braid
imu	underground oven
kapa	tapa, cloth made from the bark of the mamaki or wauke trees
olona	native shrub with strong fibers in its bark
opelu	mackerel (fish)
pali	cliff, precipice
pili	grass used for thatching
taro	a plant, the roots of which provide poi, the starchy mainstay of the Hawaiian diet. The Hawaiian word is "kalo"
ti	woody plant of the lily family
wauke	paper mulberry (tree)

THE AUTHOR

When Frances Reed came to Hilo in 1958 she could not have guessed how her love of books would set the pattern for her life and that of her family in Hawaii. As Children's Librarian of the Hawaii County Library for ten years, she became familiar with the local legends and used them in storytelling hours. In 1962 the Reeds established Petroglyph Press and began publishing Hawaiiana, including the reprinting of several books of legends. Retirement from the library was followed by several years of retail and wholesale book business and now, retired again, Frances combines her love of books and travel in searching the mainland for out-of-print Hawaiiana which she resells through Bookfinders of Hawaii.

THE ILLUSTRATOR

Jan Moon arrived in Hilo in 1960 and soon established herself as an artist and teacher of art. Her love of nature and close observation of it led to the writing and illustrating of her first book, "Living With Nature in Hawaii." Petroglyph Press published this in 1971 and several revisions have been issued since then. Currently, she is devoting much of her time to painting fish and birds and other nature themes on silk. As a member of the Sierra Club and on her own she has hiked over all the islands and many parts of the world, gathering inspiration.